Wedding Collecti
for Keyboard

Always 2
An Old Fashioned Wedding 4
Ave Maria 6
Berenice 8
Bridal Chorus (Wedding March from '*Lohengrin*') 10
Canon In D 12
(Everything I Do) I Do It For You 14
Get Me To The Church On Time 16
I'm Always Hearing Wedding Bells 18
Marrying For Love 20
Now And Forever 22
One Hand, One Heart 24
Polovtsian Dance 26
Processional (from '*The Sound Of Music*') 28
This Is My Lovely Day 30
Trumpet Tune and Air 32
Trumpet Voluntary 34
The Vows Go Unbroken (Always True To You) 36
The Wedding 38
Wedding March 40
Wedding Song (There Is Love) 42
What Are You Doing The Rest Of Your Life? 44
Yes, Yes! (My Baby Said 'Yes'!) 46

Music arranged and processed by Barnes Music Engraving Ltd
East Sussex TN22 4HA, UK

Cover design by xheight Limited

Published 1996

ALWAYS

Words and Music by John Lewis, David Lewis and Wayne Lewis

Suggested Registration: Flute
Rhythm: Soft Rock
Tempo: ♩ = 66

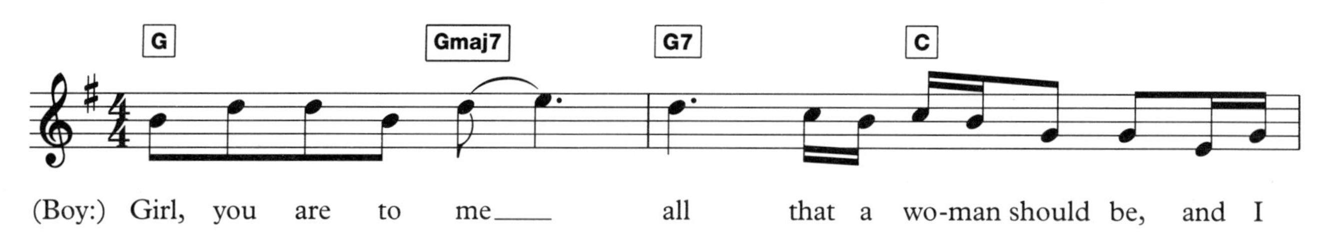

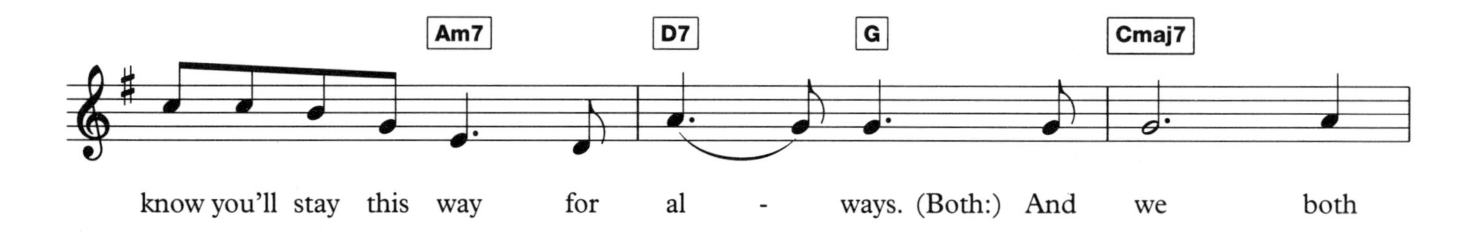

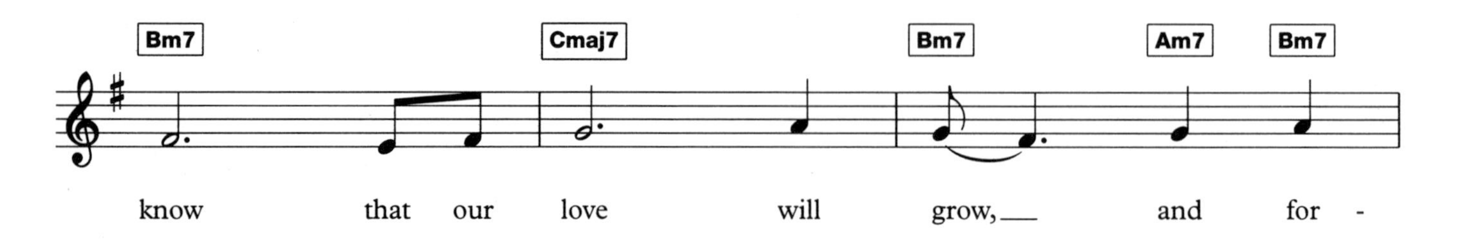

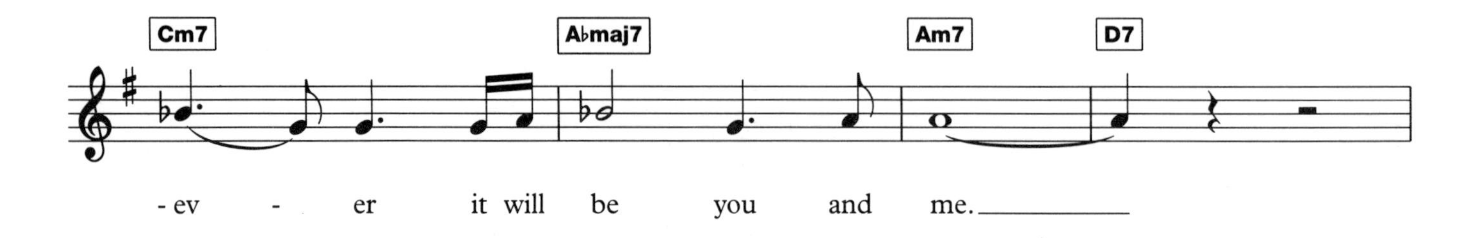

G
Gmaj7
G7
C
Ooh, you're like the sun, chas - ing all the rain a - way,
Am7
D7
G
Gmaj7
when you come a - round you bring bright - er days. You're the per - fect one for
G7
C
Am7
me, and you for - ev - er - will be, and I will love you so for
D7
G
Gmaj7
G7
C
al - ways. Ooh, ooh,
Am7
D7
G
Gmaj7
I will love you so for al - ways. Ooh,
G7
C
Am7
D7
G
ooh, I will love you so for al - ways.
A♭maj7
Am7
Bm7
C
Cmaj7
Cm7
D7
G
Gmaj7
G7

An Old Fashioned Wedding

Words and Music by Irving Berlin

Suggested Registration: Vibraphone
Rhythm: Swing
Tempo: ♩ = 160

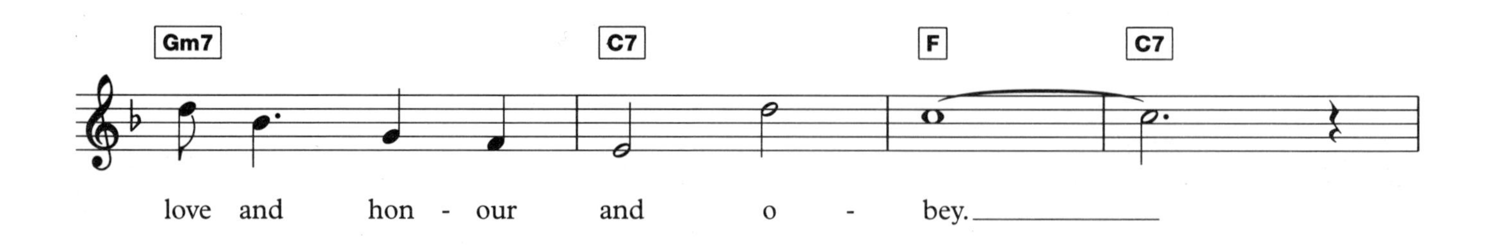

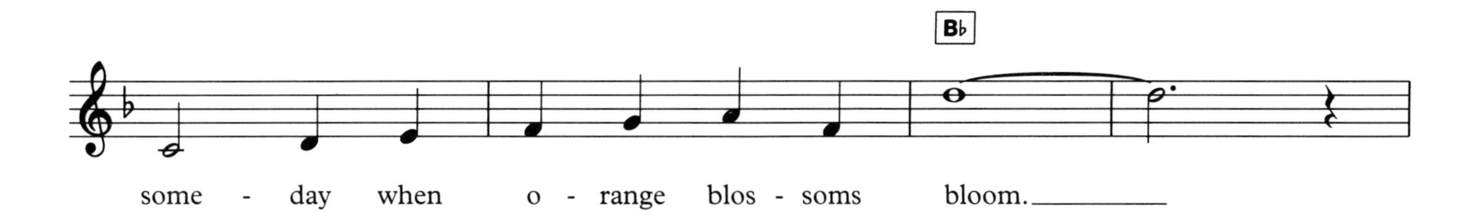
B♭
some - day when o - range blos - soms bloom.

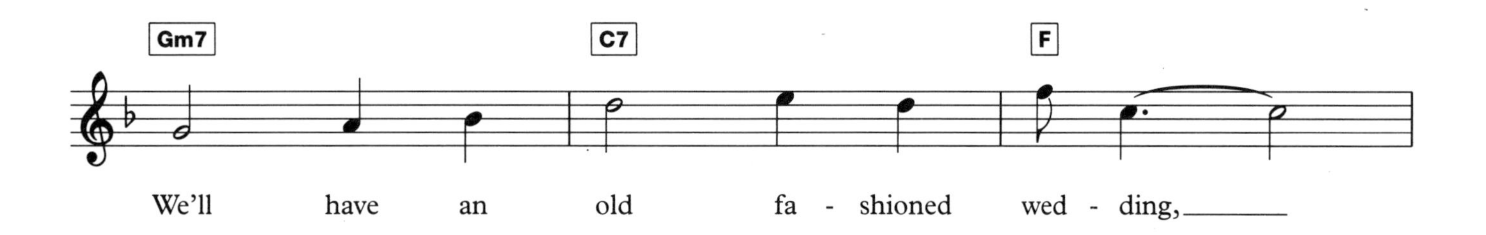
Gm7
C7
F
We'll have an old fa - shioned wed - ding,

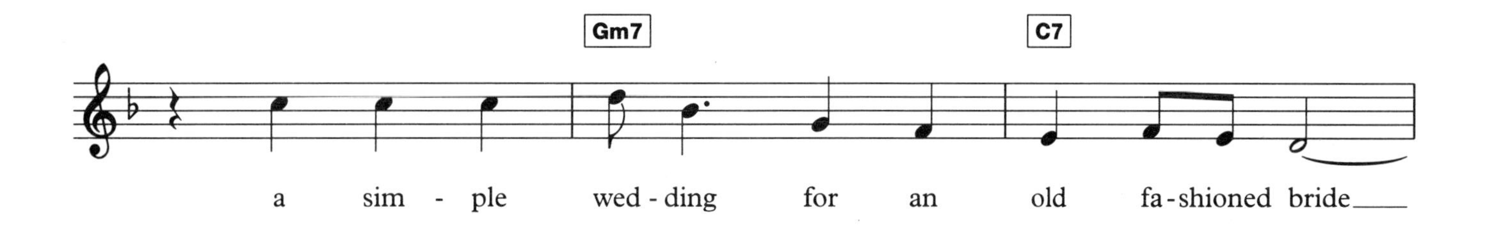
Gm7
C7
a sim - ple wed - ding for an old fa-shioned bride

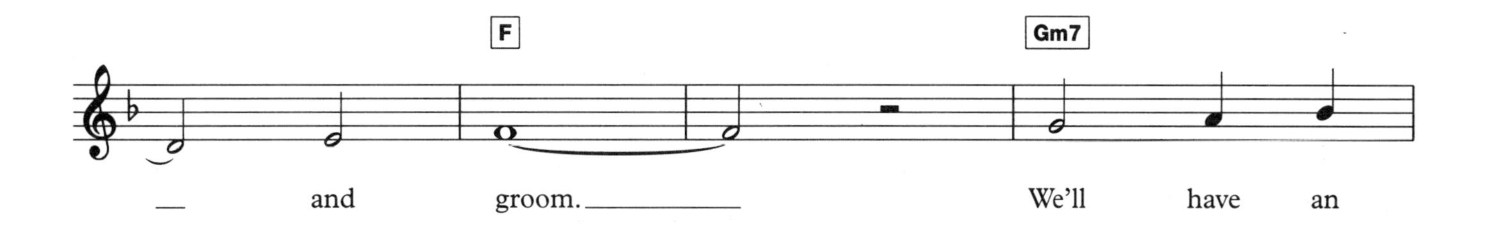
F
Gm7
and groom. We'll have an

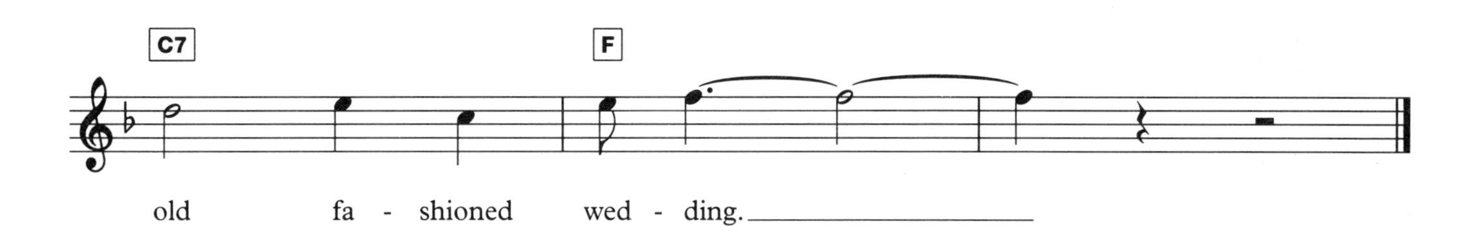
C7
F
old fa - shioned wed - ding.

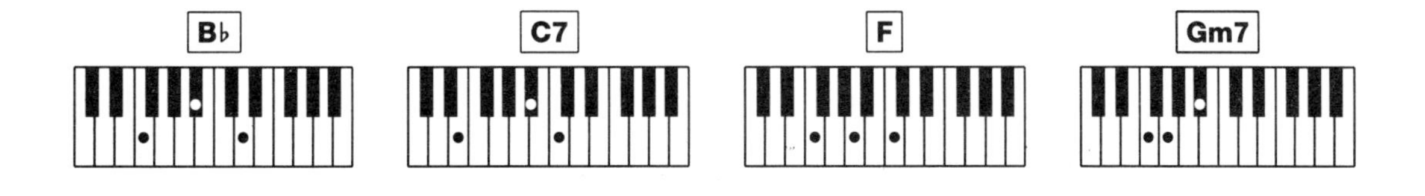
B♭
C7
F
Gm7

Ave Maria

From the First Prelude of Johann Sebastian Bach / Adapted by Charles Gounod

Suggested Registration: Choir
Rhythm: Soft Rock (rhythm off)
Tempo: ♩ = 76

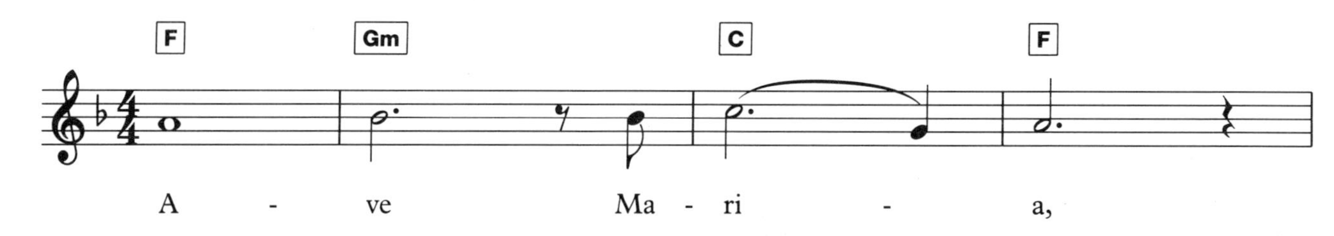

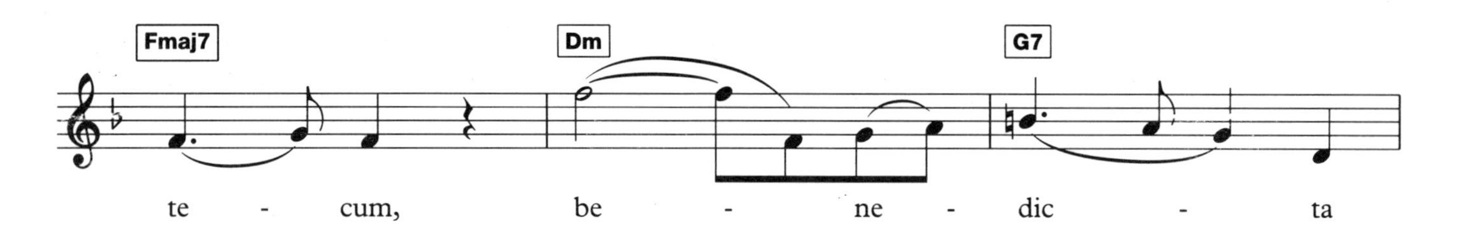

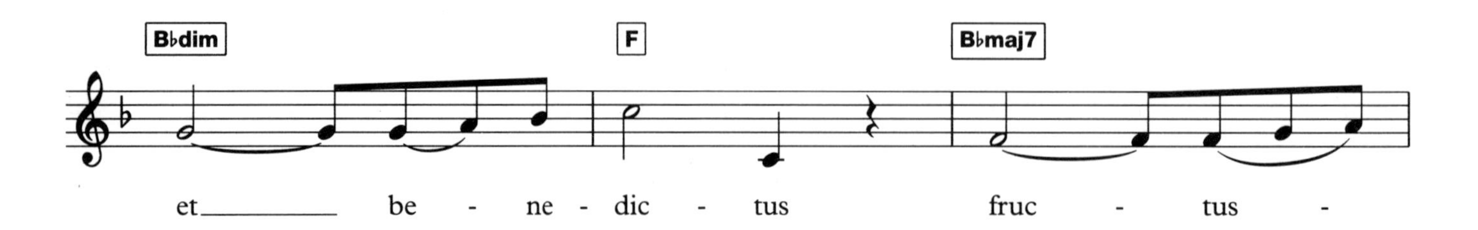

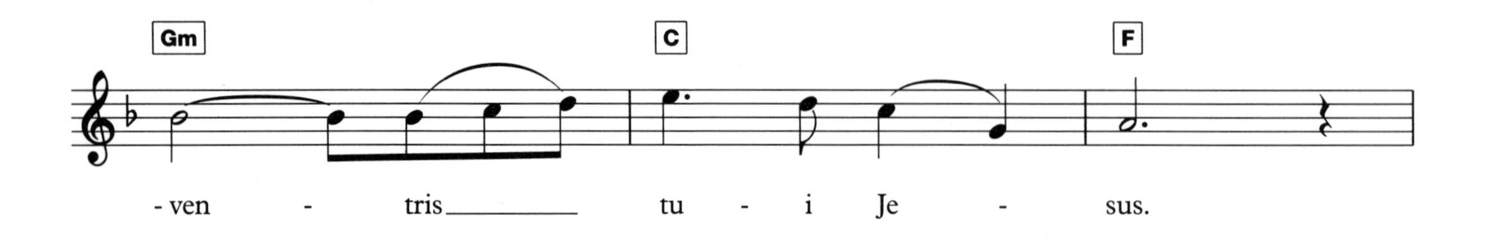

F7
B♭
Bdim
Fm
B♭m
Sanc - ta Ma - ri - a, sanc - ta Ma - ri - a, Ma - ri - a,
C
F
C
C7
o - ra pro - no - bis no - bis pec - ca - to - ri - bus,
Fdim
F
Csus4
nunc et in ho - ra, in ho - ra
C7
F7
B♭
C7
F
mor - tis nos - trae. A - men! A - men!
B♭
B♭maj7
B♭m
B♭dim
Bdim
C
C7
Csus4
Cdim
Dm
F
Fmaj7
F7
Fm
Fdim
G7
Gm

Berenice

By George Frederick Handel

Suggested Registration: Harpsichord
Rhythm: Waltz
Tempo: ♩ = 104

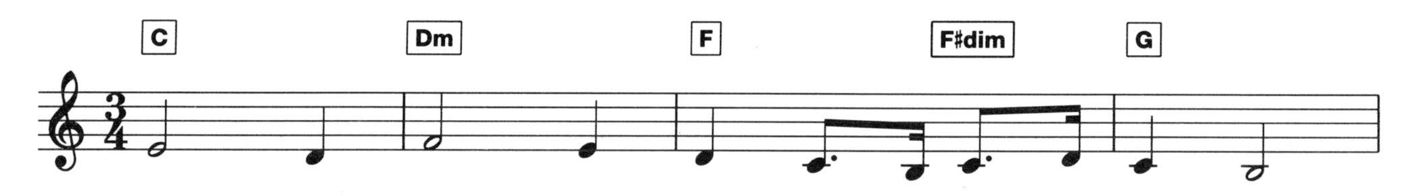

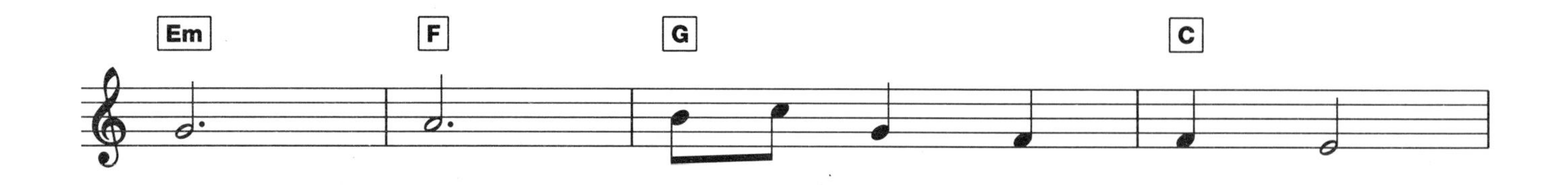

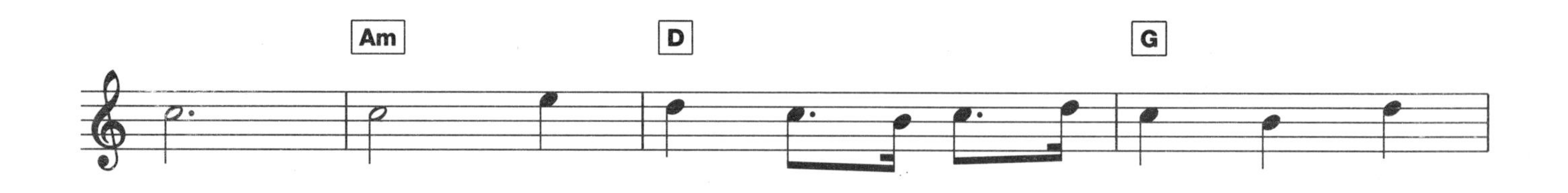

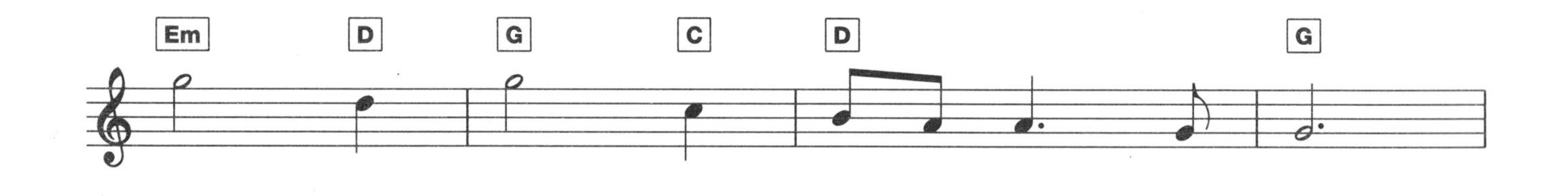

Em
F
G
Dm
F
G
C
F
G
C
Dm
F
F♯dim
G
C
G
Am
Dm
G
C
Am
C
D
Dm
E7
Em
F
F♯dim
G

Bridal Chorus (Wedding March From 'Lohengrin')

By Richard Wagner

Suggested Registration: Church Organ
Rhythm: Slow March
Tempo: ♩ = 92

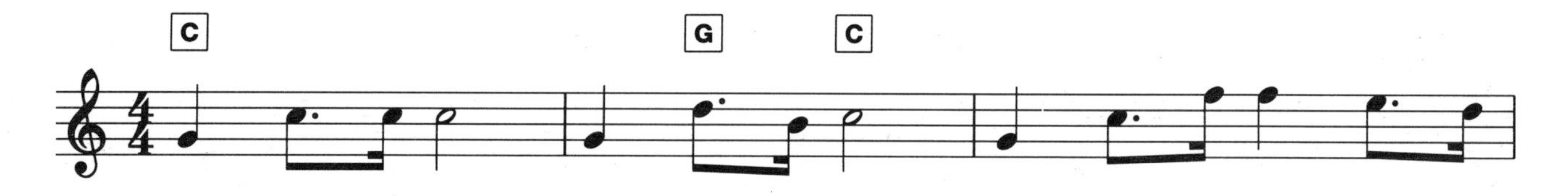

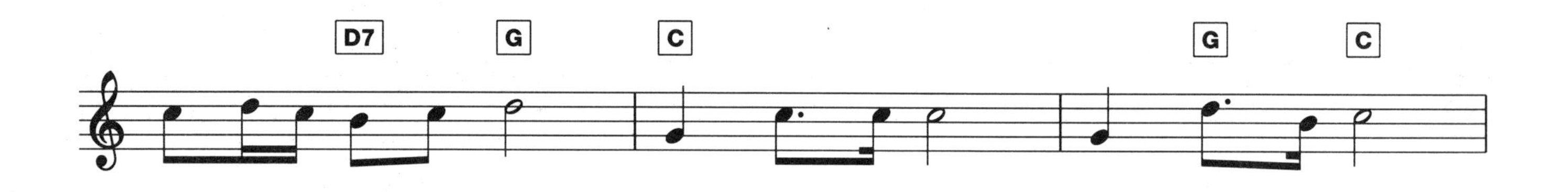

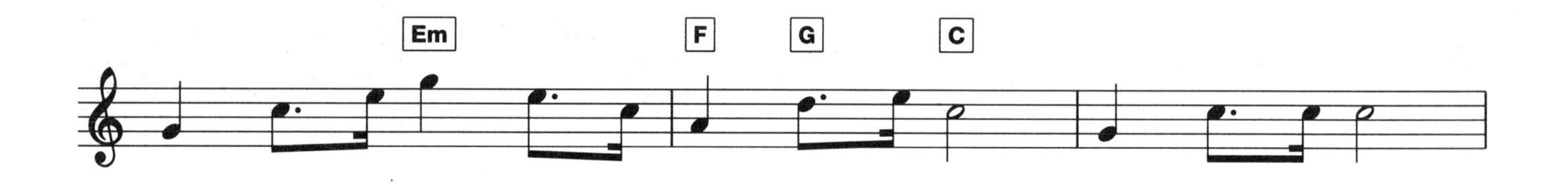

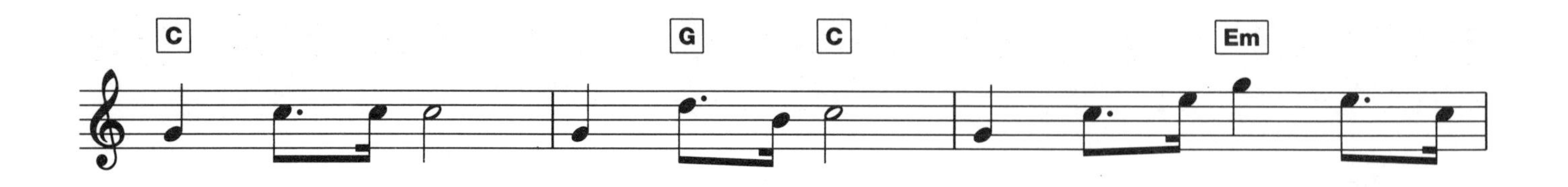

F
G
C
Dm
G
D7
G

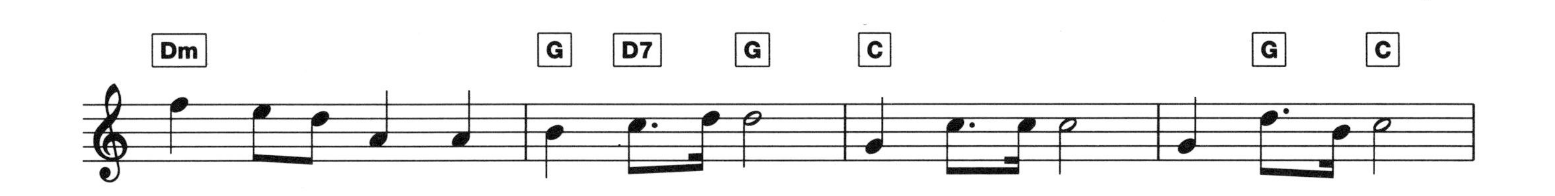
Dm
G
D7
G
C
G
C

D7
G
C

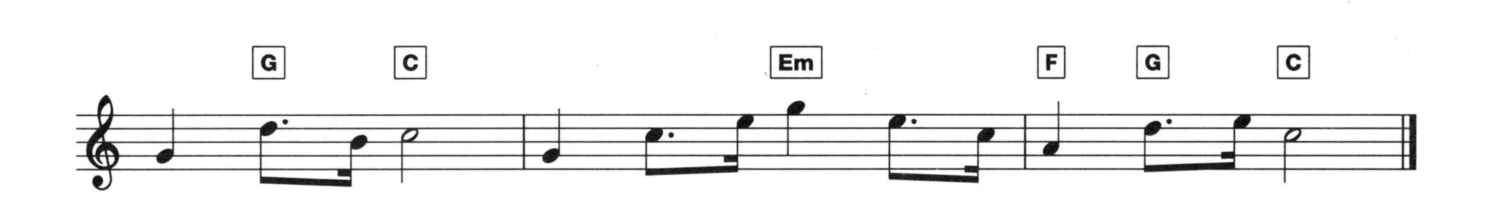
G
C
Em
F
G
C

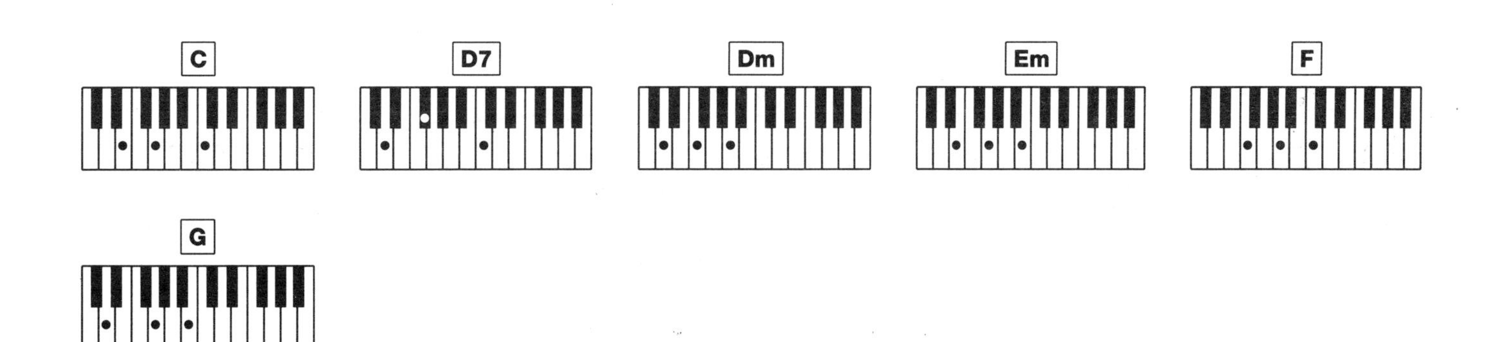
C
D7
Dm
Em
F
G

Canon In D

By Johann Pachelbel

Suggested Registration: Flute
Rhythm: Soft Rock
Tempo: ♩ = 80

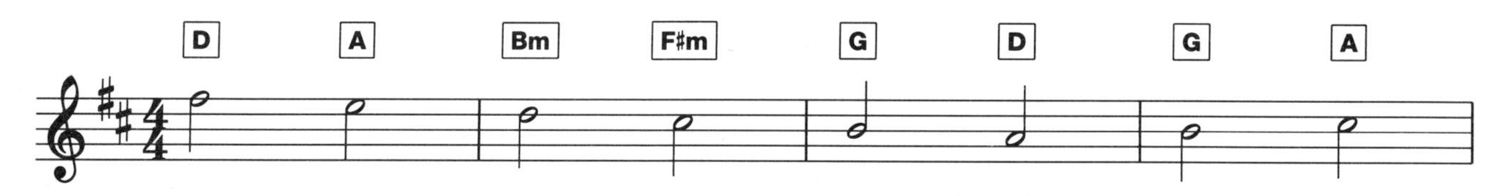

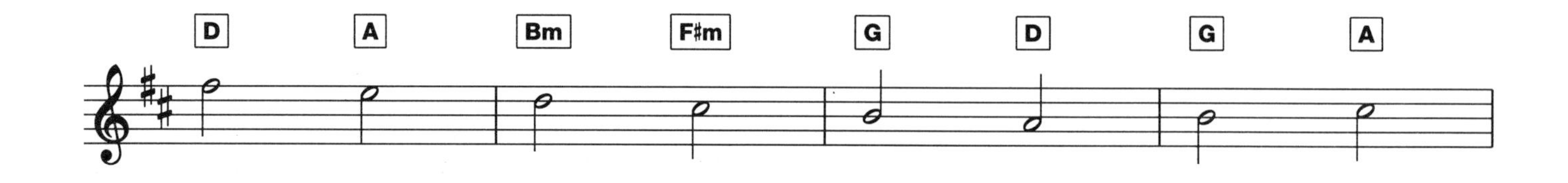

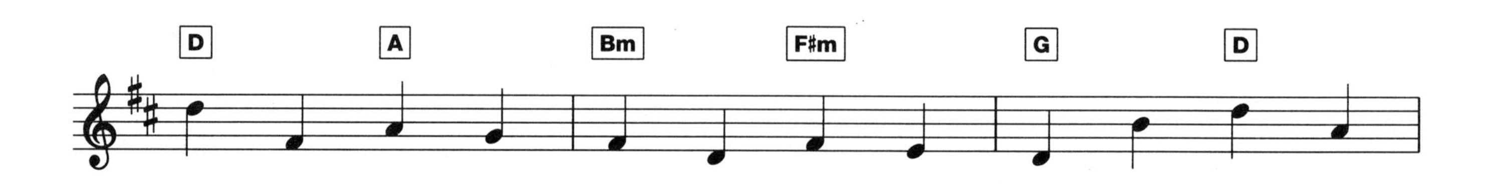

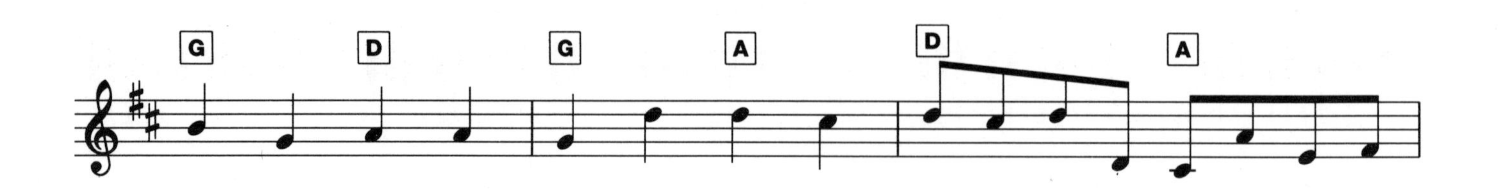

Bm
F♯m
G
D
G
A
D
A
Bm
F♯m
G
D
G
A
D
A
Bm
F♯m
G
D
G
A
D
A
Bm
F♯m
G
D
G
A
D
A
Bm
F♯m
G
D
Bm
D
F♯m
G

(Everything I Do) I Do It For You

Words and Music by Bryan Adams, Robert John 'Mutt' Lange and Michael Kamen

Suggested Registration: Saxophone
Rhythm: Soft Rock
Tempo: ♩ = 66

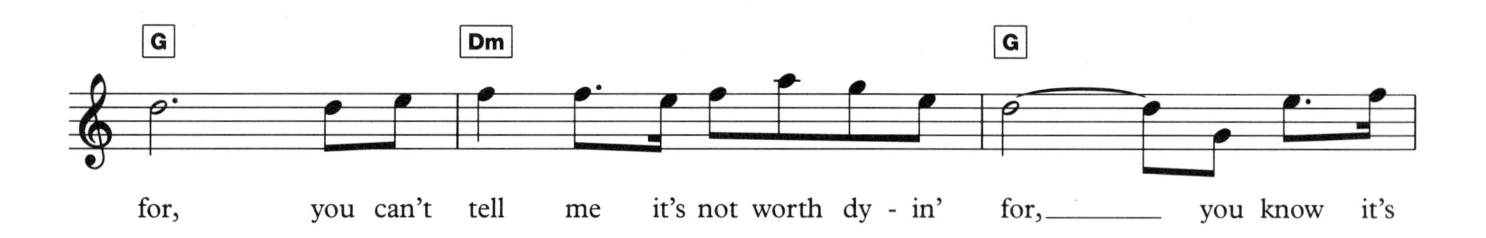

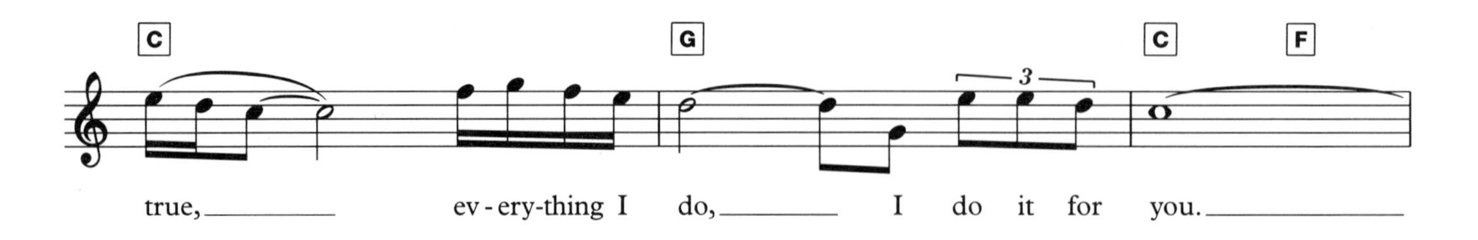

B♭
F
oth - er could give more love, there's
C
G
D
no - where un - less you're there all the time, all the
G
Dm
way, yeah. Don't tell me it's not worth try - in'
G
Dm
G
for, you can't tell me it's not worth dy - in' for, you know it's
C
G
C
F
C
3
true, ev-ery-thing I do, I do it for you.
B♭
C
D
Dm
E♭
F
G

Get Me To The Church On Time

Words by Alan Jay Lerner / Music by Frederick Loewe

Suggested Registration: Trombone
Rhythm: March
Tempo: 𝅗𝅥 = 116

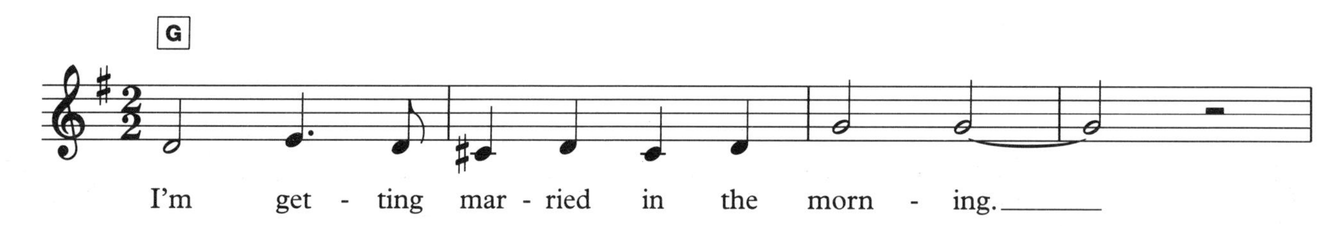

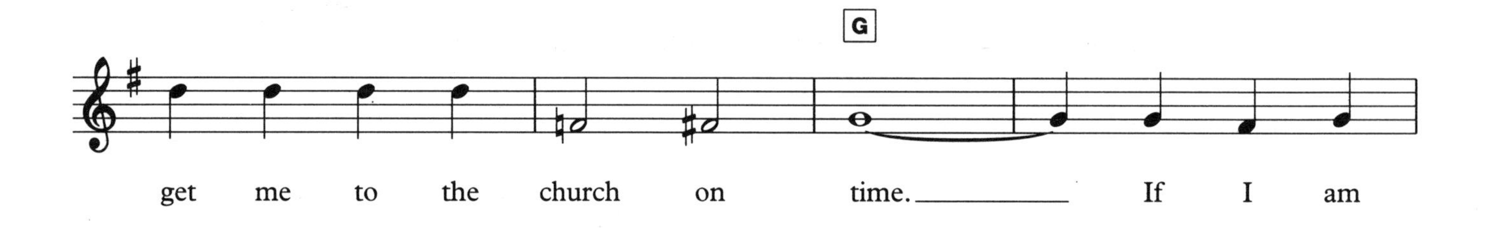

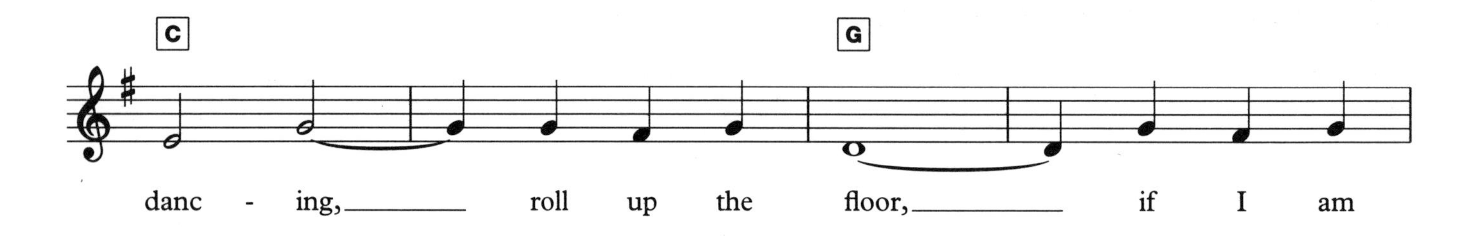

G
I'm get - ting mar - ried in the morn - ing.
Ding! Dong! The bells are gon - na chime.
D7
G
Kick up a rum - pus, but don't lose the
Bm
C
G
com - pass, and get me to the church, get me to the
Em
G
Em
Am7
church, for Pete's sake, get me to the church
D7
G
C
G
on time.
A7
Am7
Bm
C
D7
Em
G

I'm Always Hearing Wedding Bells

Words by Robert Mellin / Music by Herbert Jarczyk

Suggested Registration: Vibraphone
Rhythm: Swing
Tempo: ♩ = 160

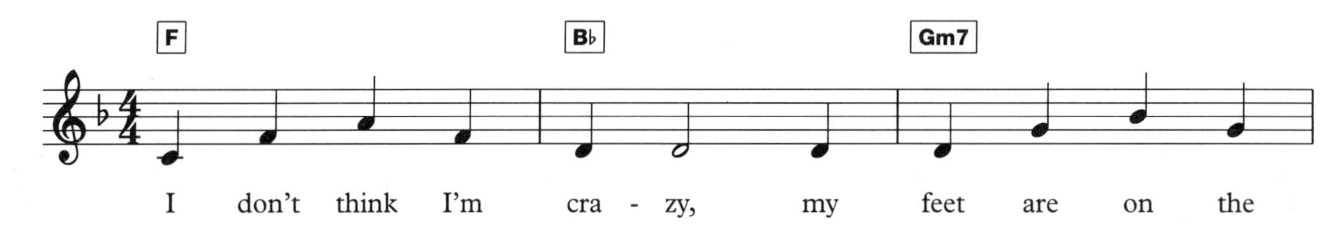

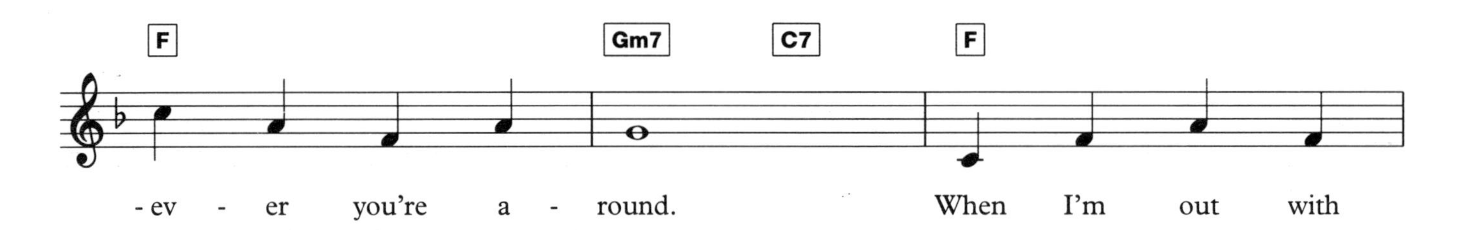

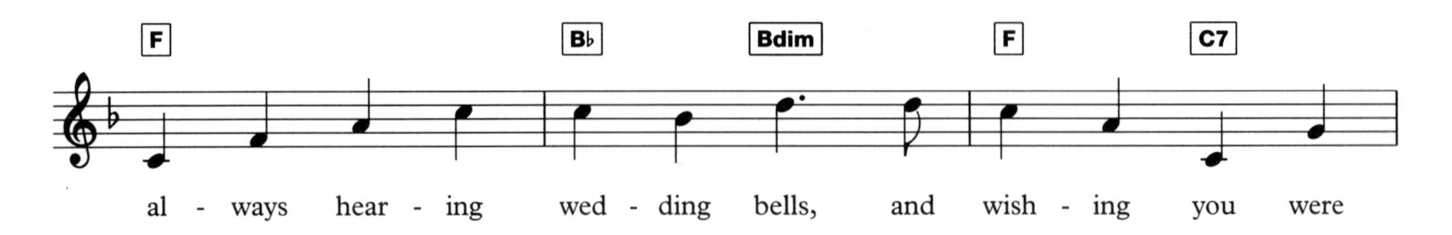

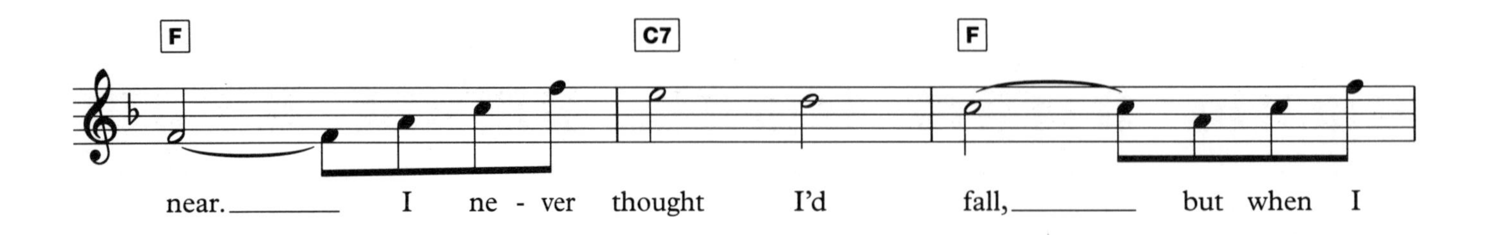

C7 F C7
saw you, how quick - ly I fell, and dar - ling, that's not
F Dm7 G7 Gm7 C7
all, your kiss rang a wed - ding bell.
F B♭ Gm7
If I'm on - ly dream - ing, you'll make those dreams come
C7 F
true on the day I'm hear - ing
B♭ Bdim F C7 F
wed - ding bells, walk - ing down the aisle with you.
B♭ Bdim C7 Dm7 F
G7 Gm7

Marrying For Love

Words and Music by Irving Berlin

Suggested Registration: Strings
Rhythm: Swing
Tempo: ♩ = 138

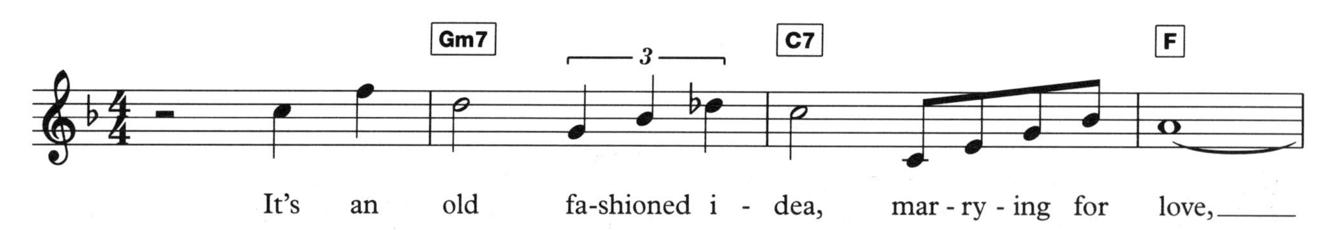

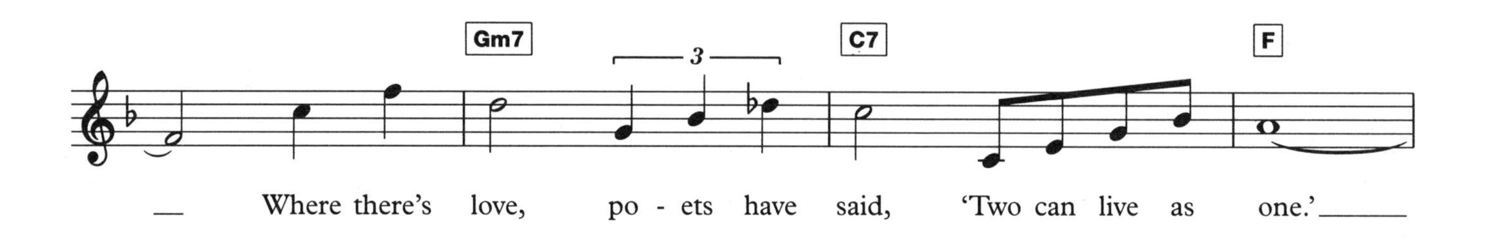

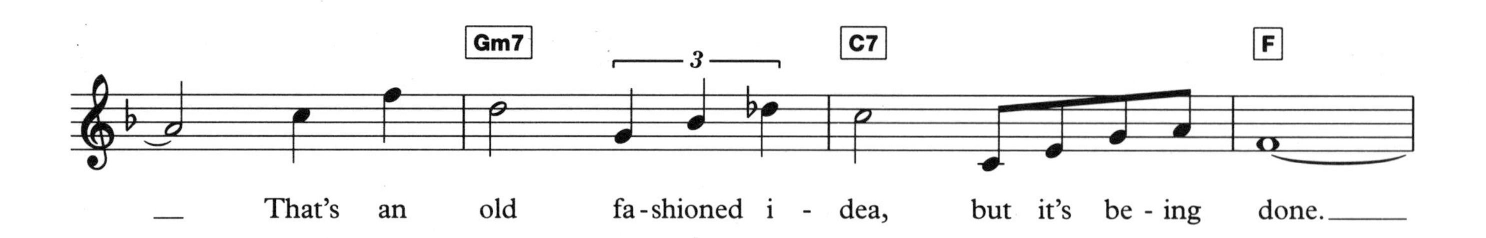

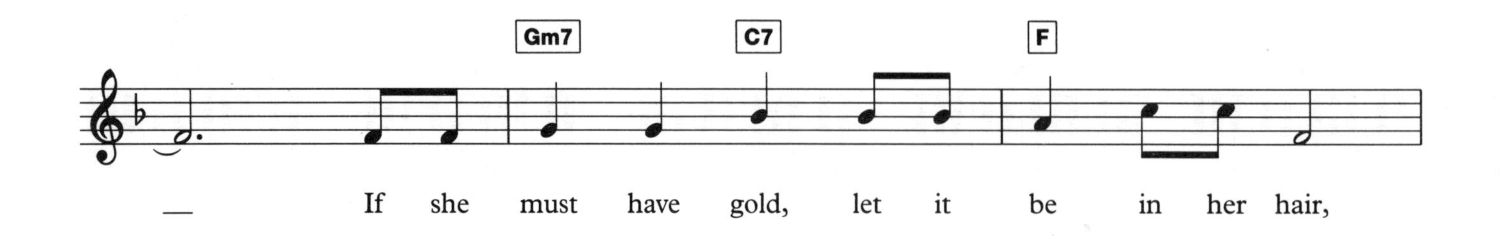

Gm7
E♭
F
A
ru - bies, let them be in her lips, dia - monds,
E7
A
F
let them shine in her eyes. Just an
Gm7
C7
Dsus4
D7
old fa-shioned ro - mance, with a moon a - bove, a ro -
Gm7
C7
Dm
- mance, one that will end mar - ry - ing for love,
B♭
F
C7
F
that's the kind of love that I'm think - ing of.
A
B♭
C7
D7
Dsus4
Dm
E♭
E7
F
Gm7

Now And Forever

Words and Music by Richard Marx

Suggested Registration: Electric Piano
Rhythm: Soft Rock
Tempo: ♩ = 104

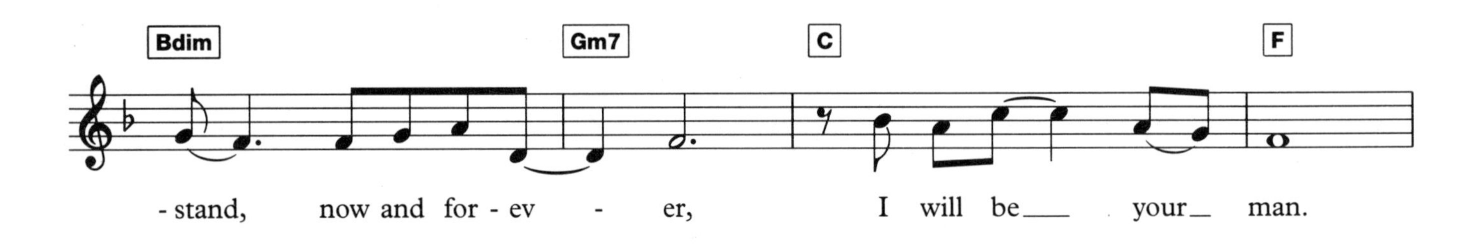

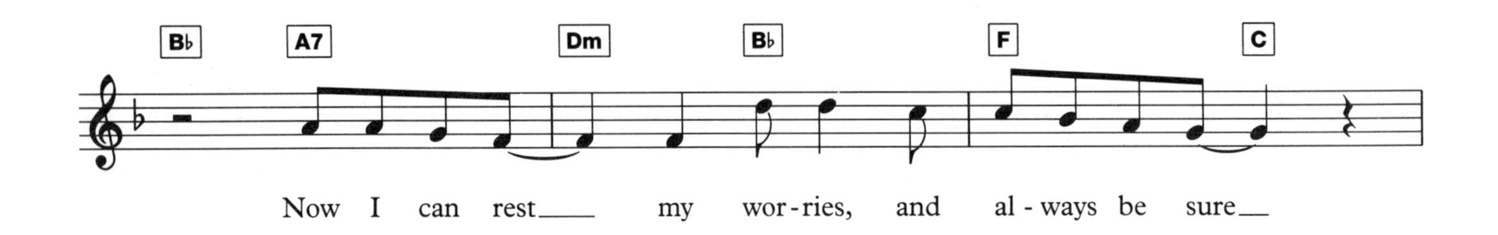

Dm
B♭
F
C
Dm
B♭
that I won't be a - lone___ a - ny - more. If I'd on - ly known

F
C
Gm7
B♭m
C
__ you were there__ all the time,___ all this time.___

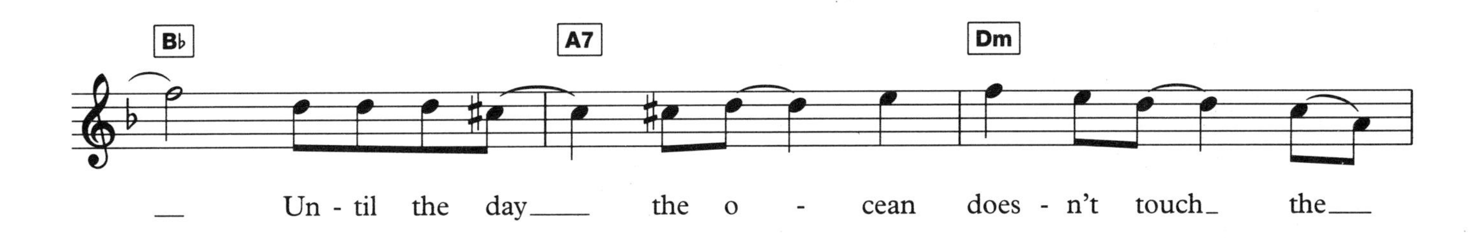
B♭
A7
Dm
__ Un - til the day___ the o - cean does - n't touch_ the___

Bdim
Gm7
C
F
B♭
F
sand, now and for - ev - er, I will be__ your man.___

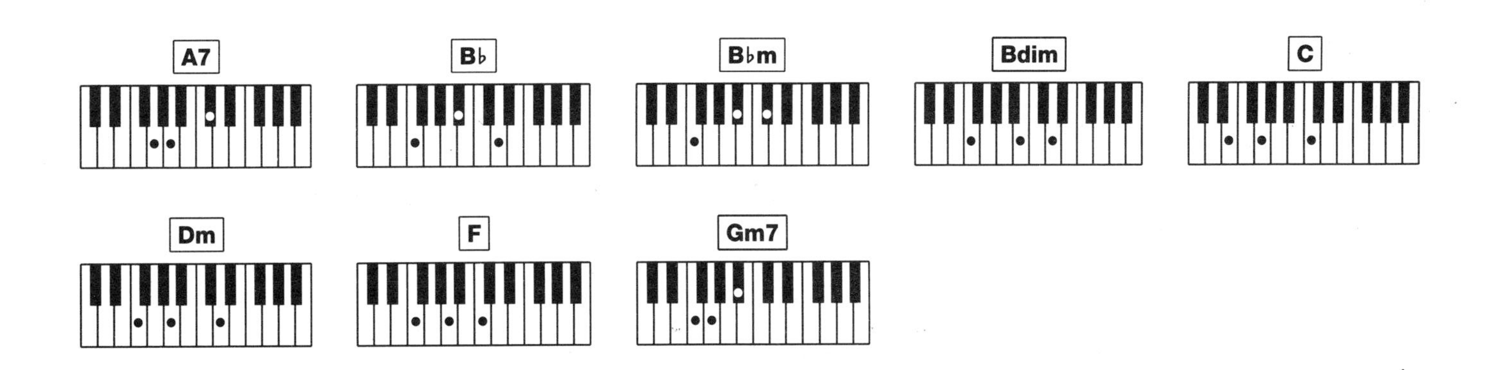
A7
B♭
B♭m
Bdim
C
Dm
F
Gm7

One Hand, One Heart

Words by Stephen Sondheim / Music by Leonard Bernstein

Suggested Registration: Strings
Rhythm: Waltz
Tempo: ♩ = 96

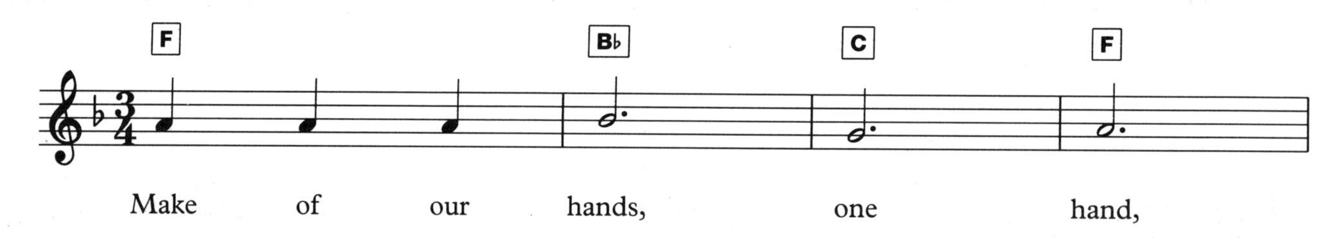

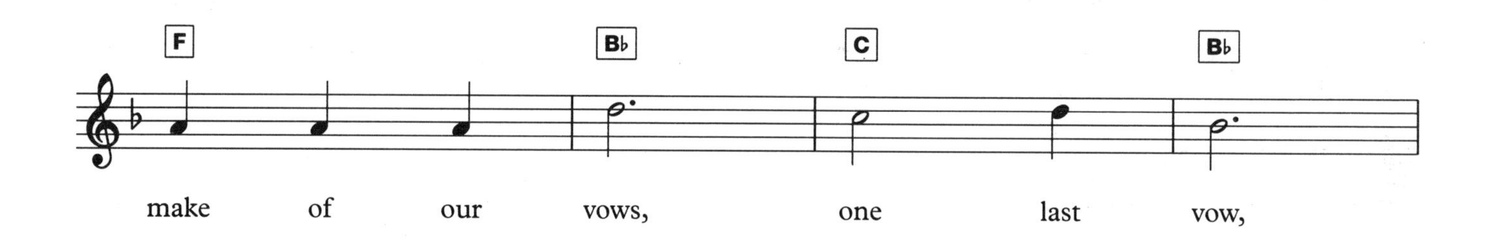

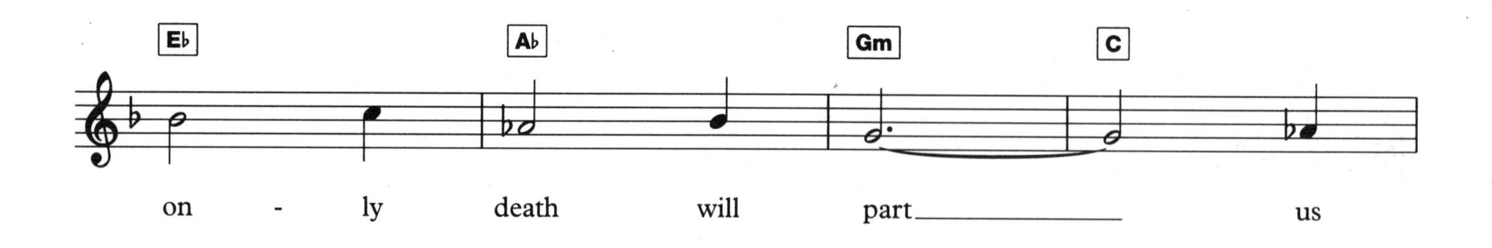

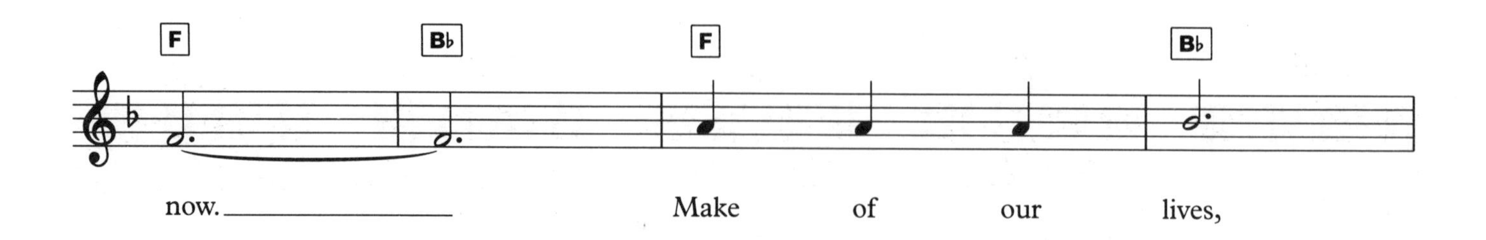

C F Dm Am
one life, day af - ter day,
Eb Bb F Bb
one life. Now it be - gins,
C Eb F Gm
now we start, one hand,
Dm Gm Eb Ab Gm
one heart, ev - en death won't part
C F Bb F
— us now.
Ab Am Bb C Dm
Eb F Gm

Polovtsian Dance

By Alexander Borodin

Suggested Registration: Flute
Rhythm: Ballad
Tempo: 𝅗𝅥 = 72

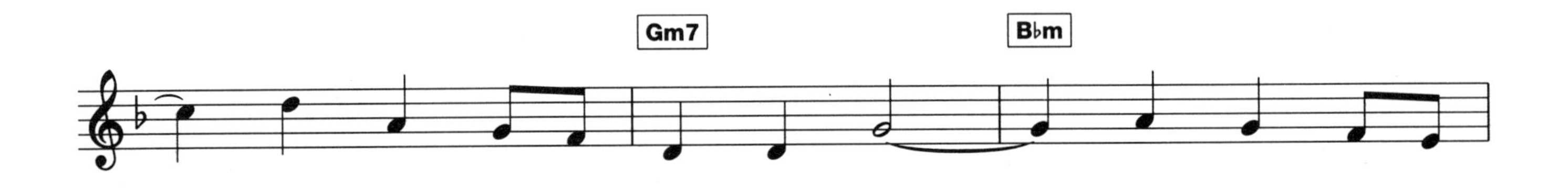

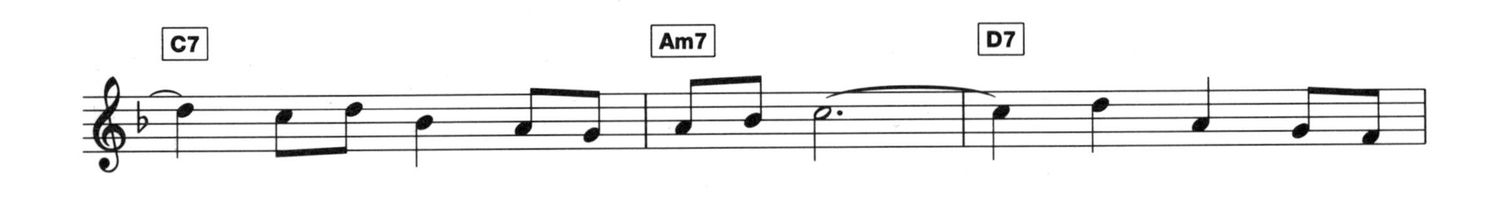

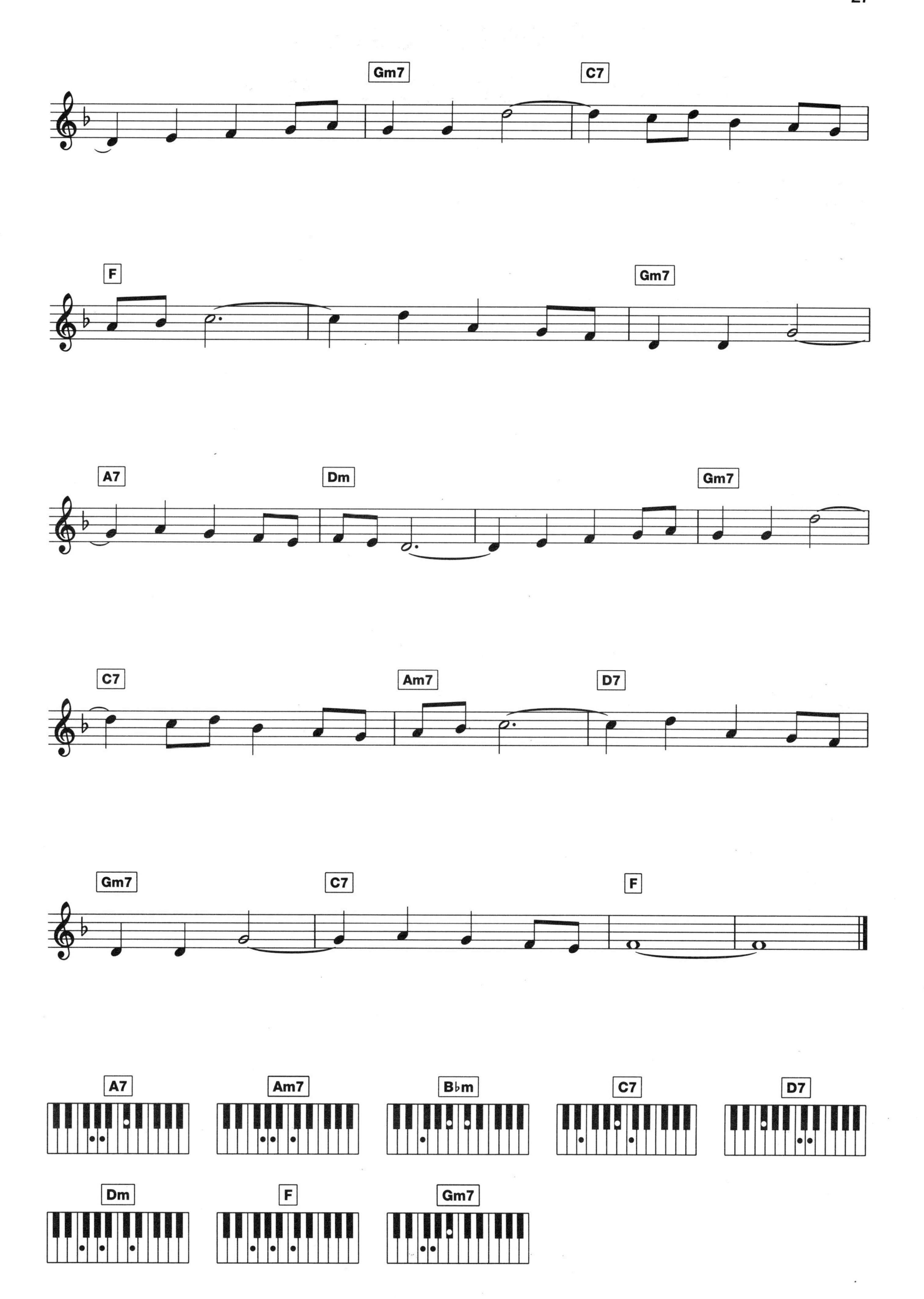
Gm7
C7
F
Gm7
A7
Dm
Gm7
C7
Am7
D7
Gm7
C7
F
A7
Am7
B♭m
C7
D7
Dm
F
Gm7

Processional (From 'The Sound Of Music')

By Richard Hammerstein II

Suggested Registration: Church Organ
Rhythm: Ballad
Tempo: ♩ = 96

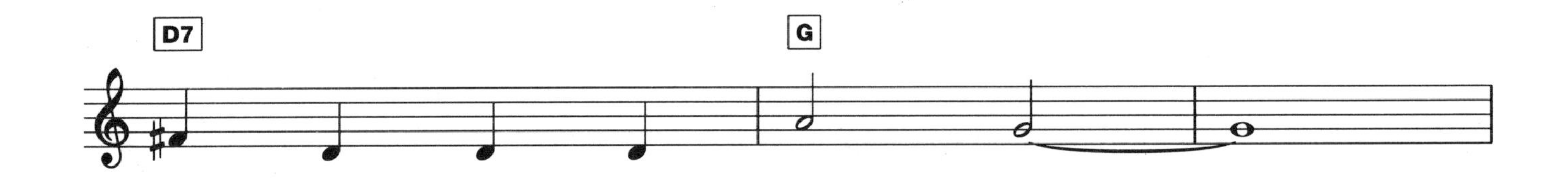

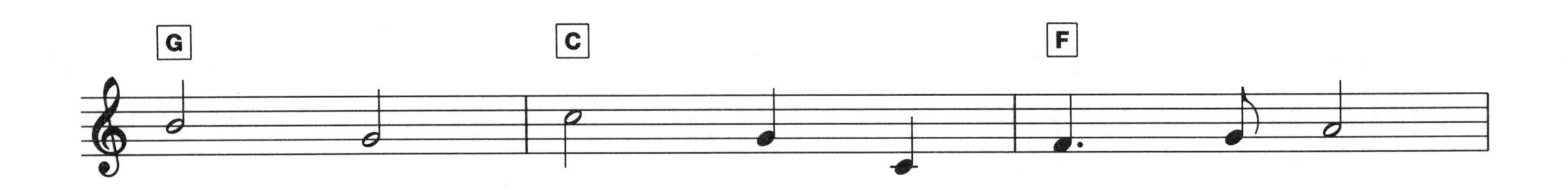

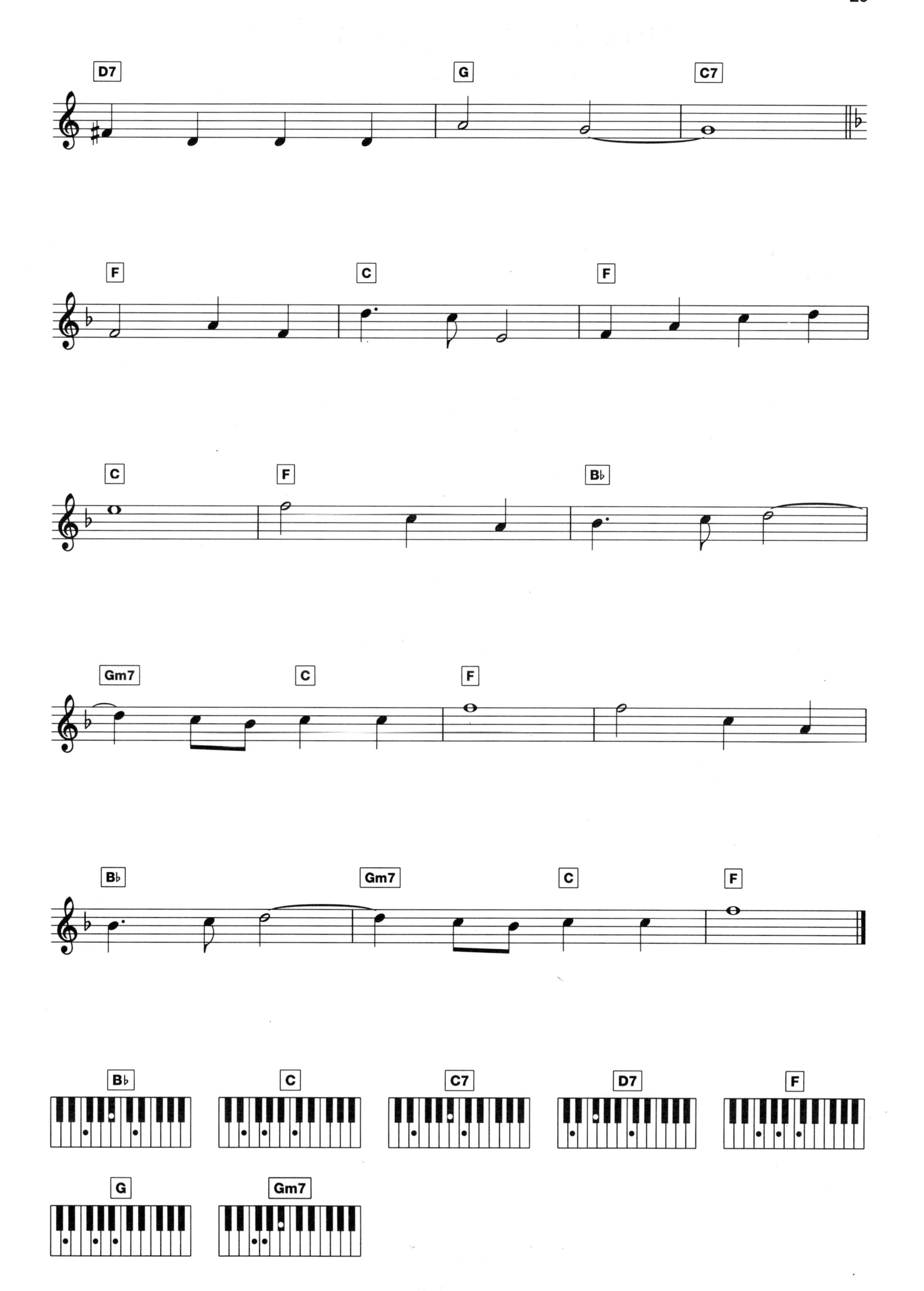
D7
G
C7
F
C
F
C
F
B♭
Gm7
C
F
B♭
Gm7
C
F
B♭
C
C7
D7
F
G
Gm7

This Is My Lovely Day

Words by Alan Patrick Herbert / Music by Vivian Ellis CBE

Suggested Registration: Strings
Rhythm: Soft Rock
Tempo: ♩ = 72

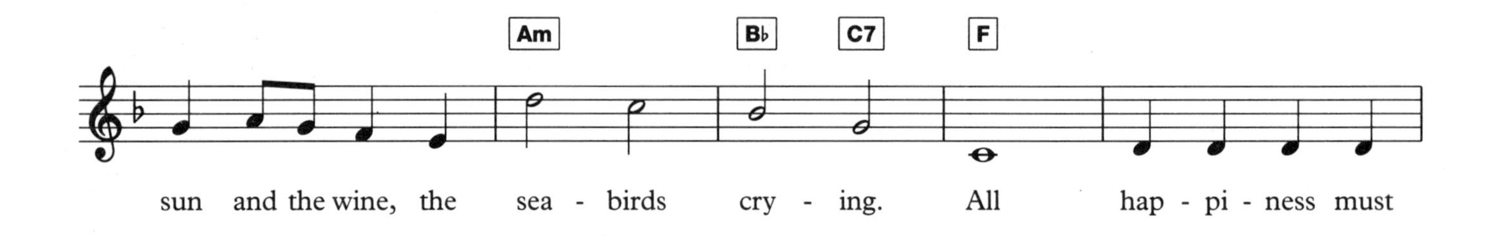

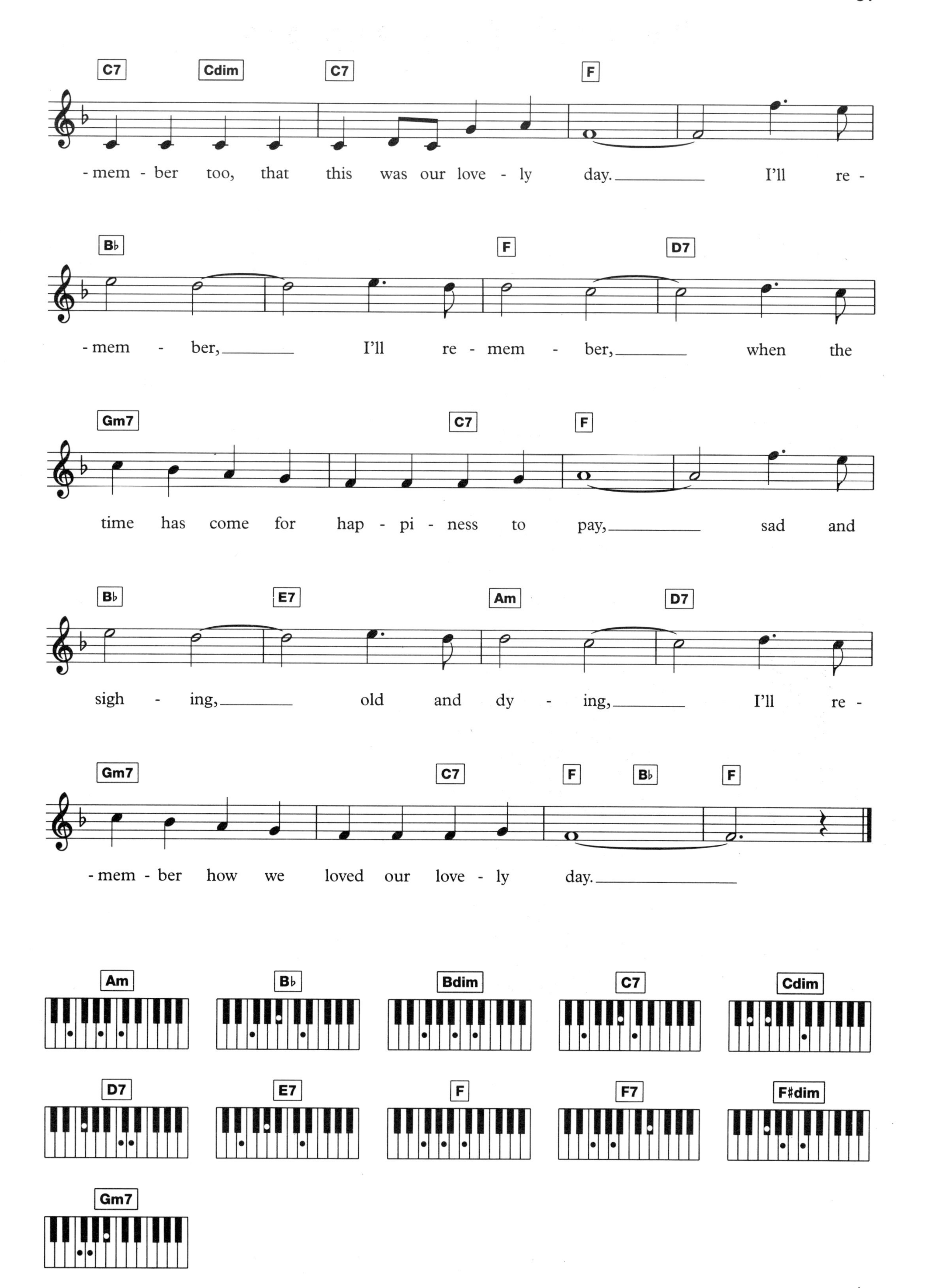
C7 Cdim C7 F
-mem - ber too, that this was our love - ly day. I'll re -
B♭ F D7
-mem - ber, I'll re - mem - ber, when the
Gm7 C7 F
time has come for hap - pi - ness to pay, sad and
B♭ E7 Am D7
sigh - ing, old and dy - ing, I'll re -
Gm7 C7 F B♭ F
-mem - ber how we loved our love - ly day.
Am
B♭
Bdim
C7
Cdim
D7
E7
F
F7
F♯dim
Gm7

Trumpet Tune And Air

By Henry Purcell

Suggested Registration: Trumpet
Rhythm: Baroque / Classical
Tempo: ♩ = 108

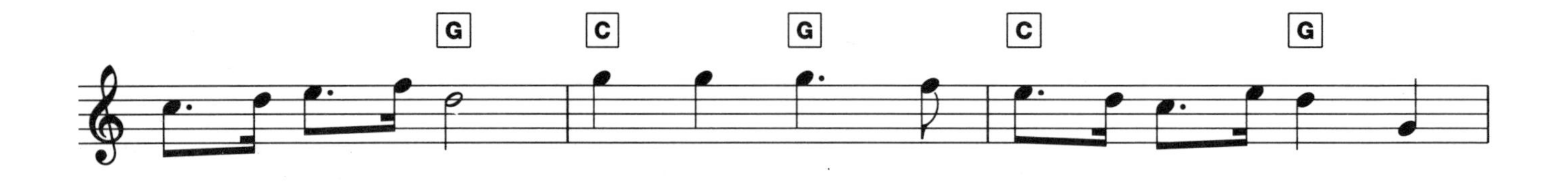

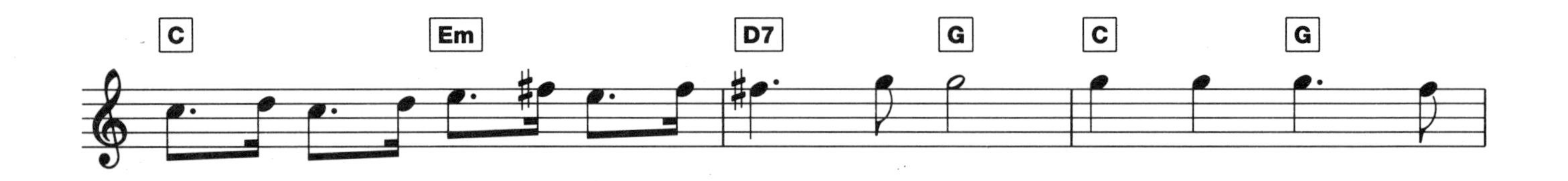

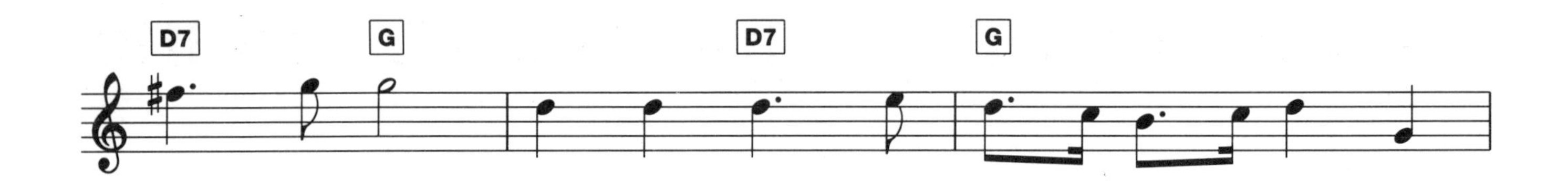

C
G
C
G
C
G
C
F
G
C
G
D7
G
C
G
C
G
C
G
C
F
G
C

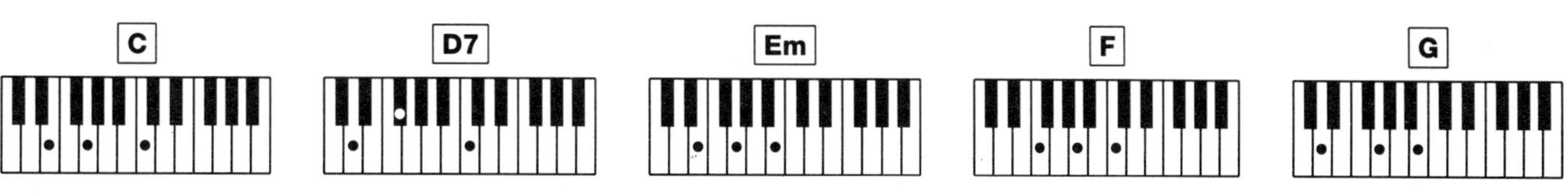
C
D7
Em
F
G
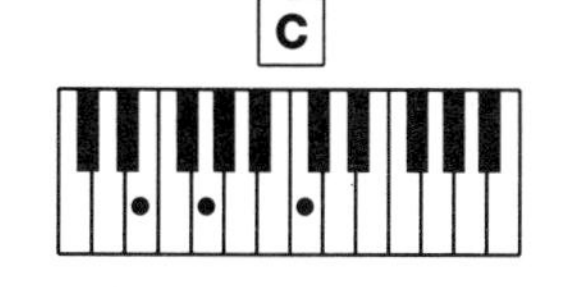
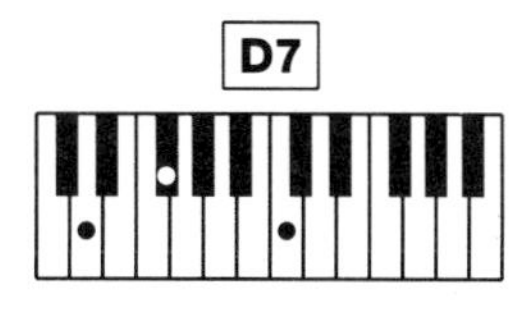
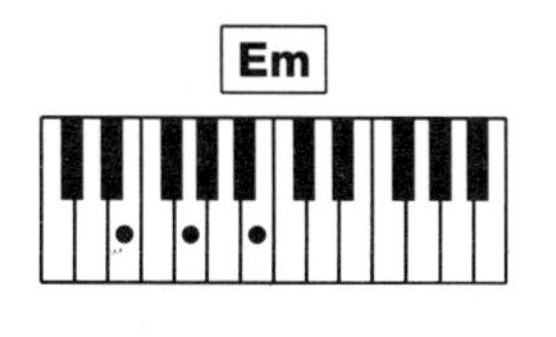
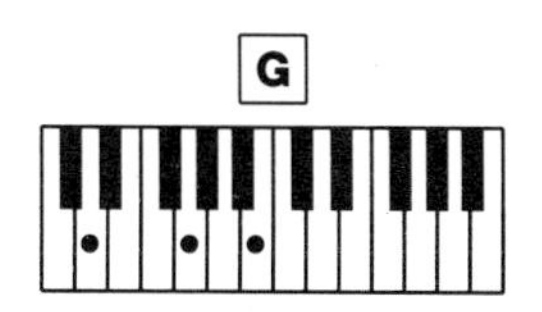

Trumpet Voluntary

By Jeremiah Clarke

Suggested Registration: Trumpet
Rhythm: Baroque / Classical
Tempo: ♩ = 104

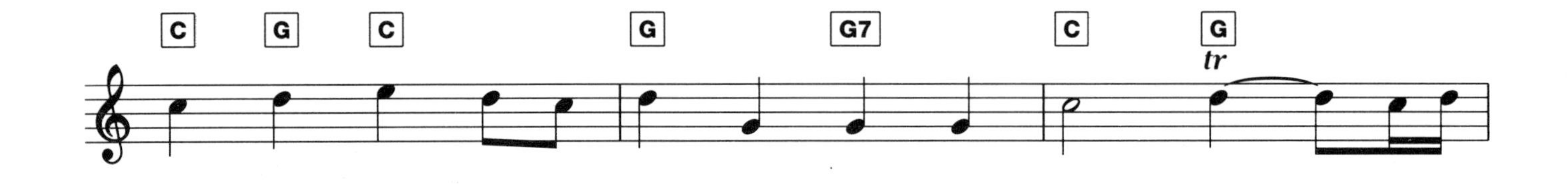

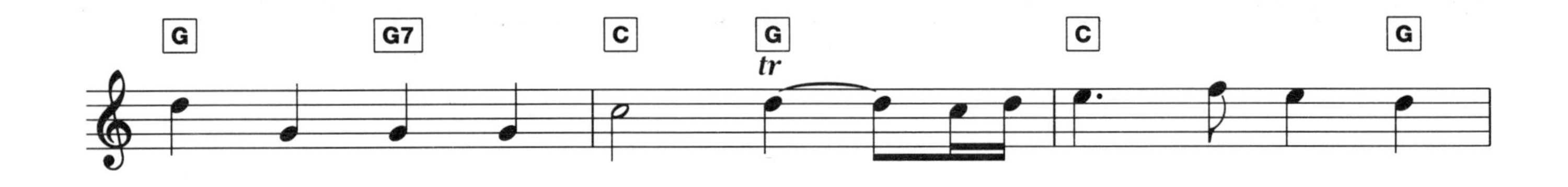

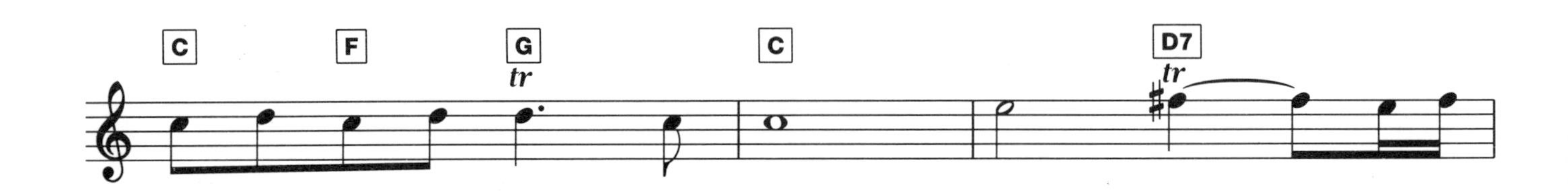

G C
D7 tr G C
G C G tr C G
C G C G G7 C G tr
C G C F G tr C

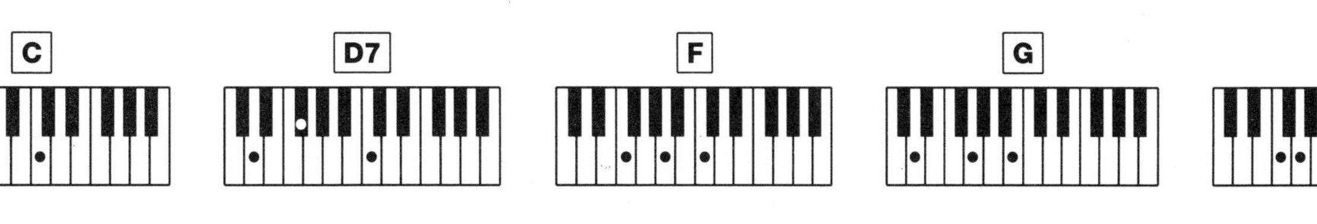
C
D7
F
G
G7

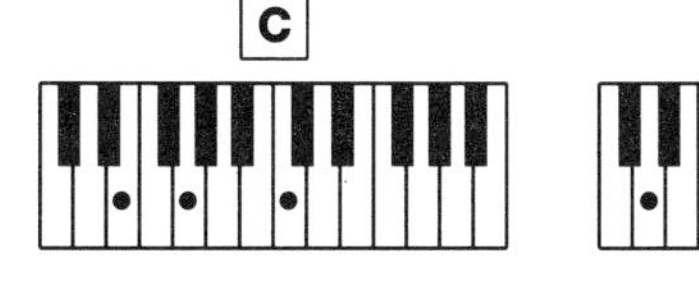

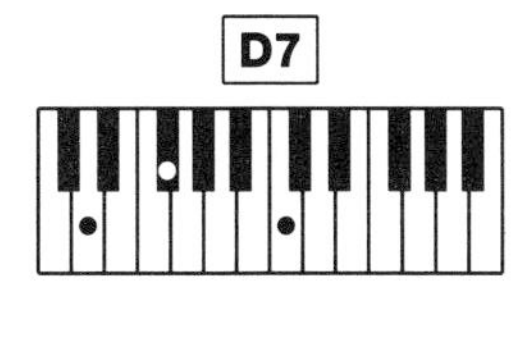

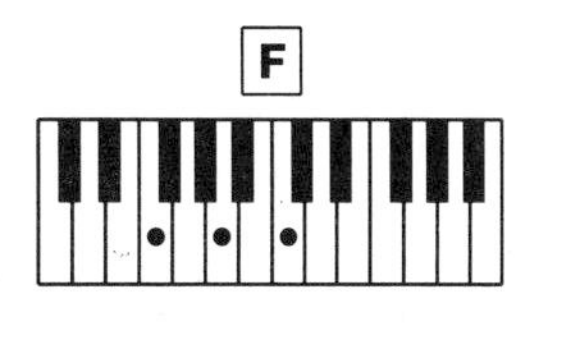

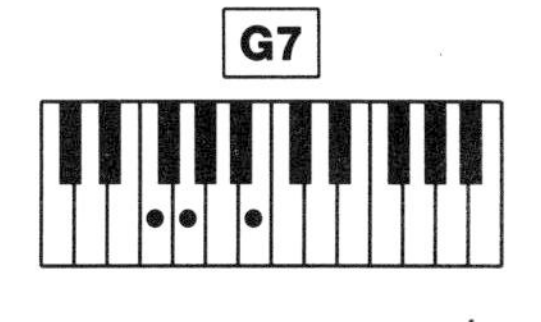

M/Night Series

The Vows Go Unbroken (Always True To You)

Words and Music by Gary Burr and Eric Kaz

Suggested Registration: Electric Piano
Rhythm: Soft Rock
Tempo: ♩ = 80

G C Am D7 G
bet - ter or worse, I'd stand by you all my life, and the
C G C F G
vows go un - bro - ken, and you still know I
C F G C F
do love, keep and hon - our,
C G C F G
al - ways true to you, love, keep and
C F C G C
hon - our, al - ways true to you.

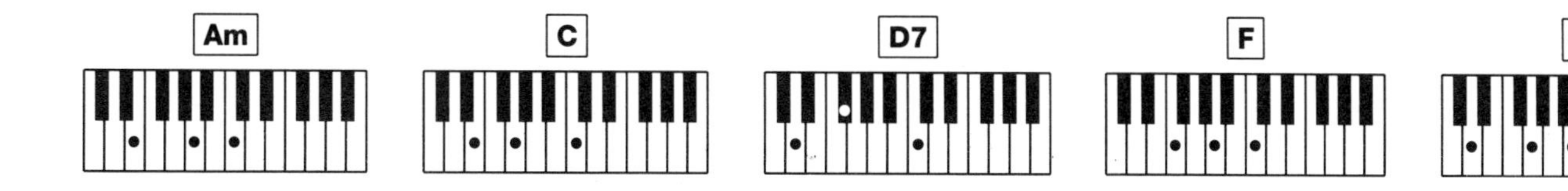
Am
C
D7
F
G

The Wedding

Original Words and Music by Joaquin Prieto / English Words by Fred Jay

Suggested Registration: Flute
Rhythm: Slow Rock 6/8
Tempo: ♩. = 72

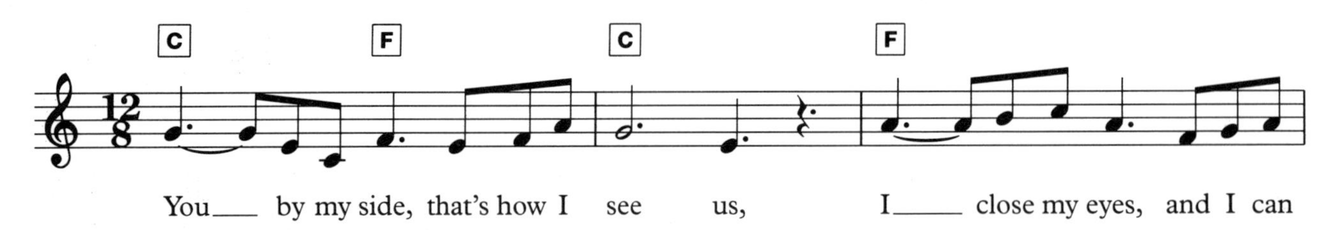

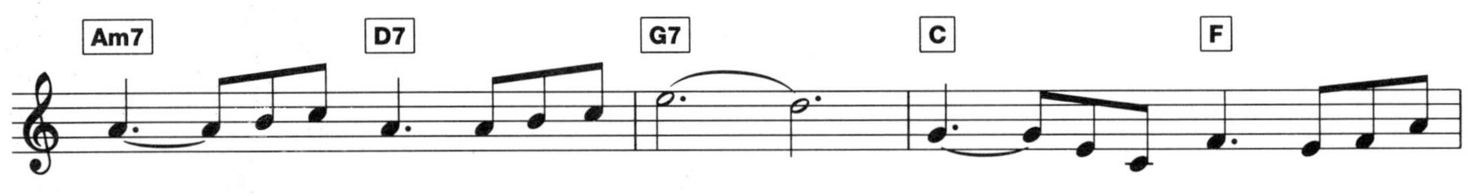

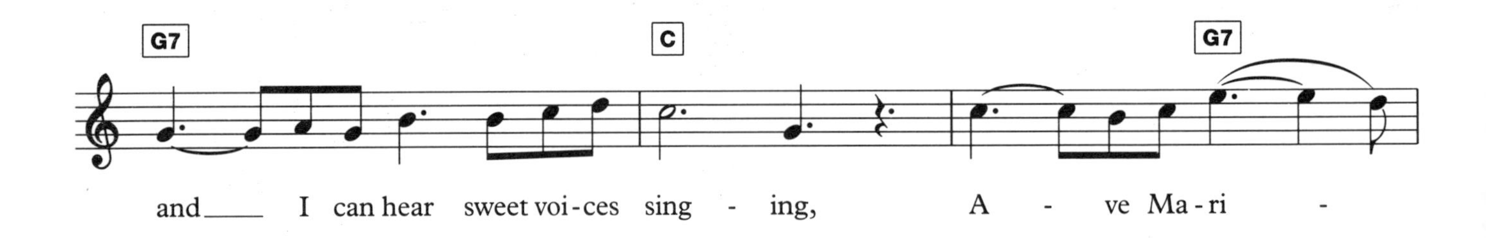

G7
C
day you'll walk down the aisle with me? Let it
Am7
D7
G
Em
be, make it be, that I'm the one for you, I'd be
Am7
D7
G7
C
F
yours, all yours, now and for - ev - er. I see us now, your hand in
C
F
C
my hand, this is the hour, this is the mo - ment,
G7
C
G7
C
and I can hear sweet voi-ces sing - ing, A - ve Ma-ri - a.
Am7
C
D7
Em
F
G
G7

Wedding March (From 'A Midsummer Night's Dream')

By Felix Mendelssohn

Suggested Registration: Church Organ
Rhythm: Slow March
Tempo: ♩ = 108

Am
B
Em
F
C
G7
C
G
C
G
C
F
F♯dim
G
Am
B
Em
F
Gsus4
G7
C
Am
B
Em
F
C
G7
C
Am
B
C
Em
F
F♯dim
G
G7
Gsus4

Wedding Song (There Is Love)

Words and Music by Noel Stookey

Suggested Registration: Electric Piano
Rhythm: Soft Rock
Tempo: ♩ = 108

F
there is love.
Well, a man shall leave his
C
Bb
F
mo - ther, and a wo - man leave her home,
Dm
F
C
they shall tra - vel on to where the two shall bc as one,
F
C
as it was in the be - gin - ning is
Bb
F
Dm
now and till the end. Wo - man draws her
F
C
life from man, and gives it back a - gain, and there is
Bb
F
love, there is love.

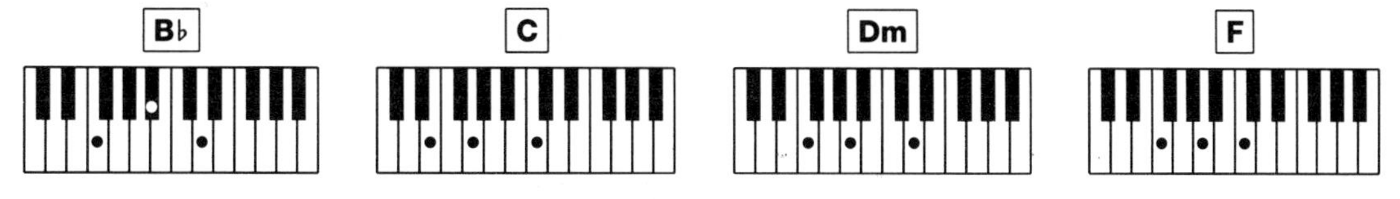
Bb
C
Dm
F

What Are You Doing The Rest Of Your Life?

Words by Alan and Marilyn Bergman / Music by Michel Legrand

Suggested Registration: Strings
Rhythm: Soft Rock
Tempo: ♩ = 84

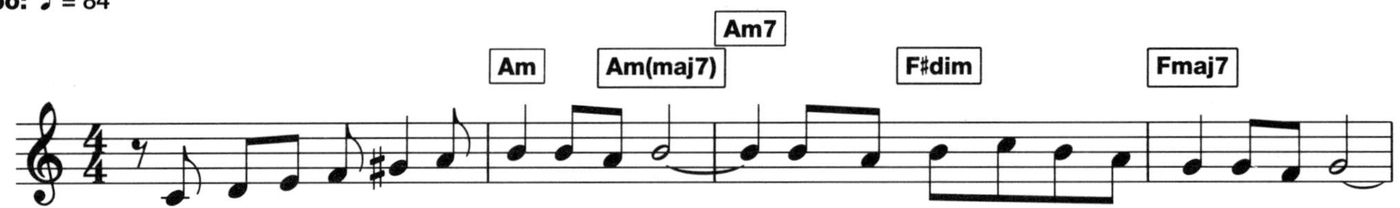

Amaj7
A♭m7
D♭7
G♭maj7
night, and when you stand be-fore the can-dles on a cake, oh, let me be the
Gm7
C7
Fmaj7
Am
Am(maj7)
one to hear the si-lent wish you make! Those to-mor-rows wait-ing deep in your eyes,
Am7
F♯dim
Fmaj7
Dm7
in the world of love you keep in your eyes, I'll a-wak-en what's a-sleep in your eyes.
Bm7♭5
E7
F
It may take a kiss or two, through all of my life,
Bm7♭5
E7
Fmaj7
summer, win-ter, spring and fall of my life, all I ev-er will re-
Am
E7
Am
-call of my life is all of my life with you.
A♭m7
Amaj7
Am
Am(maj7)
Am7
Bm7♭5
C7
D♭7
Dm7
E7
F
Fmaj7
F♯dim
G♭maj7
Gm7

Yes, Yes! (My Baby Said 'Yes'!)

Words and Music by Con Conrad and Cliff Friend

Suggested Registration: Clarinet
Rhythm: Swing
Tempo: ♩ = 184

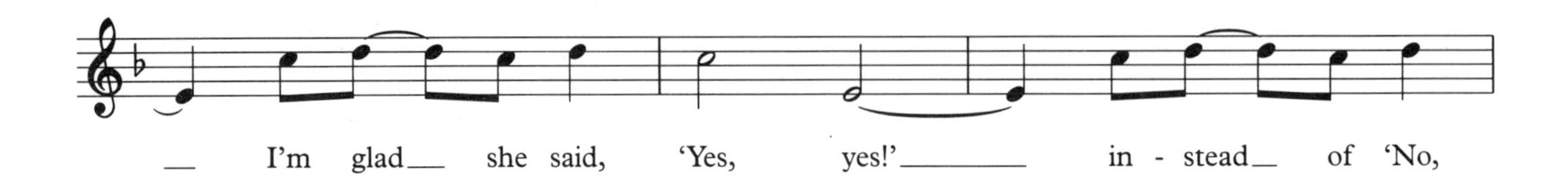

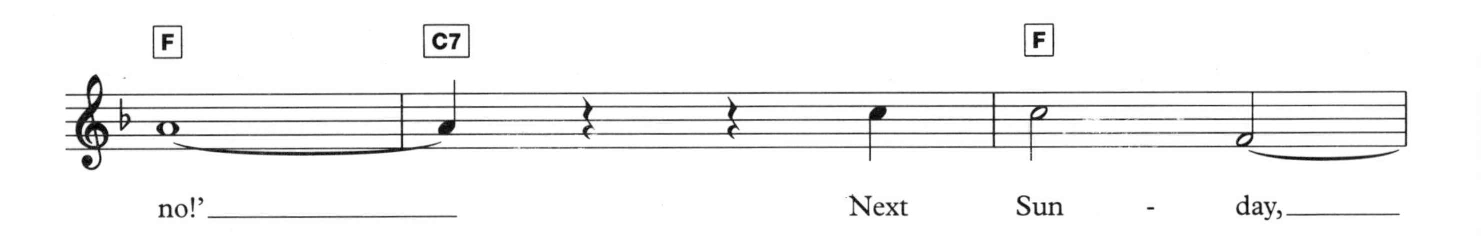

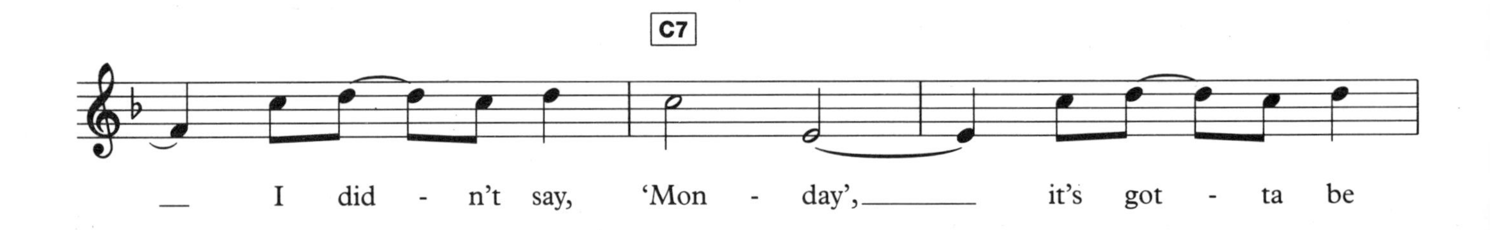

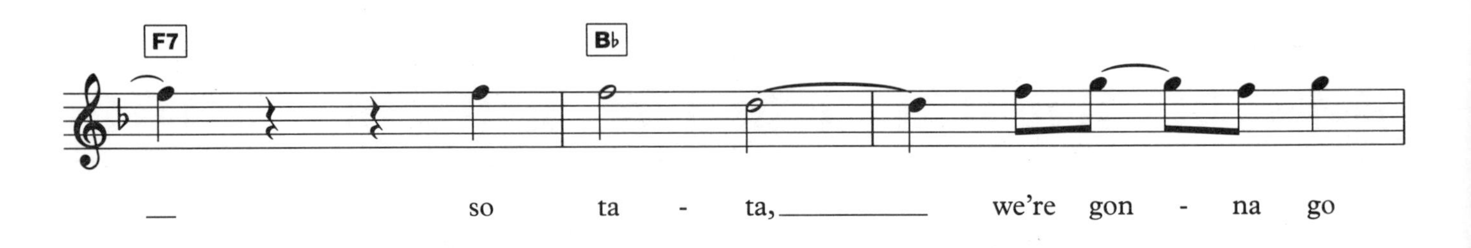

Printed by Watkiss Studios Ltd., Biggleswade, Beds. 1/96

The Easy Keyboard Library

also available in this series

Country Songs
including:
Don't It Make My Brown Eye's Blue, Just When I Needed You Most, The Rose and Stand By Your Man

Classic Hits Volume 1
including:
All Woman, From A Distance, I'd Do Anything For Love (But I Won't Do That) and Show Me Heaven

Classic Hits Volume 2
including:
Don't Go Breaking My Heart, Heal The World, My Baby Just Cares For Me and What A Wonderful World

Showtunes
including:
Anything Goes, Forty-Second Street, I Remember It Well and Lullaby Of Broadway

Number One Hits
including:
Congratulations, Moon River, Stand By Me and Without You

Film Classics
including:
I Will Always Love You, Chariots Of Fire, Aces High and Mona Lisa

Love Songs Volume 1
including:
Careless Whisper, The First Time Ever I Saw Your Face, Saving All My Love For You and True Love

Love Songs Volume 2
including:
I'll Be There, Love Me Tender, Where Do I Begin? (Love Story) and You've Lost That Lovin' Feelin'

Christmas Songs
including:
Another Rock & Roll Christmas, Frosty The Snowman, Jingle Bells and Mistletoe And Wine

Soul Classics
including:
Fever, My Girl, (Sittin' On) The Dock Of The Bay and When A Man Loves A Woman

TV Themes
including:
Birds Of A Feather, Coronation Street, Last Of The Summer Wine and Match Of The Day

Big Band Hits
including:
Come Fly With Me, In The Mood, It's Only A Paper Moon and Secret Love

THE EASY KEYBOARD LIBRARY